Lessons in
LOVE

Straight from the
Horse's Mouth

By Sonja Moore Green

Trilogy Christian Publishers
A Wholly Owned Subsidiary of Trinity Broadcasting Network
2442 Michelle Drive
Tustin, CA 92780

For information, address Trilogy Christian Publishing

Rights Department, 2442 Michelle Drive, Tustin, Ca 92780.

For information about special discounts for bulk purchases, please contact Trilogy Christian Publishing.

Manufactured in the United States of America

10 9 8 7 6 5 4 3 2 1
Library of Congress Cataloging-in-Publication Data is available.
ISBN 979-8-88738-091-9
ISBN 979-8-88738-092-6 (ebook)

Table of Contents

Foreword

This book is a love story about a real stallion that was fondly named Easter. Everyone that knew him or had the opportunity to ride him absolutely loved him. It was stated many times that Easter was the Cadillac of horses, so smooth to ride and to learn how to compete on. Easter was a real horse, and his owner/trainer is a real cowboy named Curt. All the stories about this horse are true. These are just some of the amazing things this outstanding stallion has done. Not only was Easter a very smart horse with the ability to think through situations, but he also had remarkable instincts. He always knew what to do in any circumstance that confronted him.

Easter had an incredible sense, a knowing about people, especially who to trust. Easter would work hard to please Curt, or whoever Curt let ride him. This trust was obvious to those watching.

Curt has owned and trained many horses. He has also trained horses for other people as well. He stated that he has never met a horse that is Easter's equal.

In Cowboy Curt's own words, "Easter was absolutely one of a kind. He was truly all heart."

1

The Early Years

Do you think you are smarter than a horse?

I ask that because I am a horse.

Let me introduce myself. My official name is Gentlemen's Vintage, but my friends call me Easter. I know, a weird name for a horse but come to find out, my dad's name was Easter Gentlemen, and my grandpa was Easter King. So, I am called Easter for short.

Fun fact: my bloodline contains quite the pedigree, I am told. Apparently, they are in the Hall of

Fame for Reining Horses. On my birth certificate, it says my color is grey; however, people in the horse industry call me a flea-bitten grey horse. I don't know why they say that cause I don't think I got bit by flees. I think I am handsome. I just have a lot of small brown freckles! I am also called a Quarter Horse, which is a special breed of horse. The Quarter Horse is best known today as a show horse, racehorse, reining and cutting horse, rodeo competitor, ranch horse, and all-around family horse.

I was born on March 7, 1988, to a cutting horse ranch in Texas called the 2T Ranch.

I really enjoyed those early days on the 2T Ranch. I had many friends to run and play with in the soft, tall, and grassy pastures. I had all the grass that I wanted to eat or lay down on. I had plenty of room to kick up my heels and play chase.

I heard those cowboys behind the fence call us "yearlings" without a care in the world. A "yearling" is a horse that is between 1 to 2 years old. We are too young to work yet, so we just play all day, and that was fine with me.

Our pasture was right beside this black trail (I

later heard the cowboy call this a highway). There were moving objects on this trail that we could watch for entertainment if we got bored. Some moved fast, some went slow. Some made loud noises, and some had really bad smells. My friends and I did not get too close to the black trail because it was loud, scary, and full of surprises.

One day, a storm blew in and brought lots of rain. It was so much fun playing in the rain. We ran through the puddles, splashing water everywhere. We were busy playing until two of the objects on the black trail ran into each other. I think the cowboys called the objects cars. Parts were flying all over the place, and some even landed in our tall grass! I heard people's voices coming from the black trail, and all the cars on the trail stopped moving. We watched to see what was going on.

Suddenly, this larger red object with flashing lights showed up making a loud noise. It was different than the cars that crashed. The cowboys called this a truck. The people from the red truck were trying to get the crying people out of the pileup of cars. They were using loud tools, and people were working very hard to help the people crying! My friends and I were very curious. We started moving closer to the highway to get a closer look. Then, from out of nowhere, comes this big bird down from the sky. It landed in our pasture! The men from the big red truck carried the people from the crash and put them inside the bird.

When the bird began to take off, it made a whirling sound. The wind began to blow hard enough to make my tail go sideways. This startled me and my friends. We started running and bucking, trying to get out of the way.

That is when something bad happened to me.

One of my friends kicked me! I know he did not do it on purpose; he was scared like me. After the kick, I could not run or even walk! It hurt so bad that I immediately fell to my knees in the soft, wet grass. I could not get up, so I just laid there.

One of the cowboys saw me lying there and ran over to check on me.

I heard him say, "Oh no, this is bad, looks like Easter has broken something. Maybe his leg or his shoulder."

He called for this special cowboy, the one they

called "Doc." I found out later he was an animal doctor, a veterinarian. I was glad to see him because I was hurting bad. I was really scared, and I still could not move.

I heard one of the other cowboys say, "No one will want him now, he can't even walk!"

Then Doc replied, "Boys, we better not count him out yet. He is young and strong. Let us see how this break heals. I will come back to check on him in a few days. You boys make sure he gets plenty of food and water and medicine for the pain."

Well, it didn't take too long until I was able to stand again, but I could not run and play chase like I did before. Something was different. I now walked with a limp.

I hoped I wouldn't have the limp the rest of my life. I wanted to run and play again. I made the decision right then to exercise, stretch my legs, and work on running again. I did not want anyone to think I couldn't play, even with a limp.

Now, this ranch was known for selling horses to cowboys for competitions in reining and cutting. Lots of cowboys came looking. They would come up to the fence, look at me and all my friends, and ask to see my friends but never me.

The cowboys that worked on my ranch would say, "What about this one? He's a Quarter horse with an excellent pedigree (family tree)."

But still, no one wanted to look because I limped. They would simply shake their heads no. My friends all started leaving the pasture, headed for new homes, but I stayed. It got kind of lonely in the pasture all by myself.

I was not going to let my limp keep me from getting a new home! I was determined to run again.

I stayed in the pasture, alone, which gave me lots of time to exercise. I started noticing changes in my stride. At first, I just trotted slowly. Every day, I would push a little harder. Soon, I was running slowly without it hurting. Funny thing, I did not limp when I ran, only when I walked.

I was not the only thing changing. The pasture was changing as well. The grass was no longer green. In fact, it crunched under my feet. Sometimes, it was so dry that it made me sneeze! Then slowly, after the new year arrived, new friends started arriving, more "yearlings," the cowboys said. The grass was turning green and soft again and so good to eat. It was fun having new friends to play with, even though I was much bigger and older than they were. This time, I was able to play and run. My hard work had paid off!

Then one sunny day, this cowboy walked up to the pasture.

He leaned on the fence. He was talking to Tommy, my owner. I could not hear what they were saying, but he kept looking at me, not the others, ME! What was he saying? I moved closer so I could hear.

This guy was different than the other cowboys that had come to look. He did not talk loud or cuss. He had the kindest eyes, a calm voice, and a very gentle touch. I found myself walking toward him. I felt an immediate connection with him. He reached over and touched my head, he rubbed my back, he even looked at my feet! No one had ever done that before.

He had this thing in his hand called a halter. He asked if he could put it on me. I had never had one of those halter things put on my head before, but he was gentle and talked to me the whole time. It didn't hurt, just felt weird having something on my nose and under my chin.

Tommy then said, "Curt, if you can load him in your trailer, you can have him! He really needs a good home."

I got so excited to think I might be getting a new home like my friends had. I did not want to mess this up. I had never been in a trailer before. I saw them on the black trail, but I had never been this close to one. This cowboy named "Curt" led me with a rope attached to the halter to his trailer. He let me look inside and sniff it.

Then he asked, "Well Easter, do you want to go home with me?"

I sure did! So, I jumped in the trailer. He shut the door behind me, and off we went for our very first adventure down the black trail.

Love Lesson:

In this first chapter, the kind of love that was shown is called unconditional love. What everyone else saw as a broken, worthless horse, the cowboy saw as a value, and a life worth living. He did not care what Easter became or what he could do. He was just going to love him.

2

School Days

As soon as my cowboy got me home to Tucson, Arizona, a new adventure began. He called this training. I would learn something new each and every day.

What? You didn't think horses go to school? How do you think I got so smart?

He started with something called the basics. I had to learn how to walk connected to a lead rope, how to follow a lunge line, what queues to watch for, and what certain sounds meant. I had to learn what meant "go," and what meant "whoa" (which means stop). He put this thing in my mouth called a bit. The bit was connected to leather reins. These reins allowed Curt to control the direction I would go in. It took some getting used to having the bit in my mouth. Soon, I felt comfortable and was even able to eat and drink with it in my mouth.

Now, Curt did not believe in rough and tough training. He was kind, gentle, and caring, but also firm. He was blessed with animal magnetism; all animals loved him. He had a way of training that I understood, a real connection.

He also used a training style called Parelli. Parelli is a basic training for humans and horses that is based on mutual communication, and respect and trust between the trainer and horse. It is a natural horsemanship concept. With this Parelli method, a horse learns while playing games. There are seven games to teach the important concepts. Curt utilized this style with some modification and his own personal touch to complete the basic training. I really had fun and didn't even realize that I was learning!

Once the basics were mastered, he began what he called the "real training." This training included ropes and cows! He taught me how to not fear the rope circling around my head or around my feet. He taught me patience. He taught me how to chase a cow, catch a cow, and cut a cow from a herd. This kind of training he called ranching. He told me I would for sure benefit from this training and get to use it in the near future.

Curt also taught me how to have fun on a trail ride. He taught me what to watch for while riding to keep us safe. Most of all, he taught me how to act instead of reacting. I learned to stay calm. Sometimes, he would run at me with weird objects just to see if they scared me, but I stayed calm. As a reward after training, he would take me on a nice long trail ride just to relax and cool down. Everything he did was with purpose. He was always looking for educational opportunities.

The next phase of training involved introduction to mounted shooting. Mounted shooting is a sport where a cowboy rides a horse on a course shooting ten blanks (no bullet, just gun powder) at ten targets. This event is a timed event. There are penalties if you miss a target, knock over a barrel, drop a gun, or don't run the course in the correct order. I knew that I could learn the riding aspects of this sport, but having a gun go off right by my ear was going to take some getting used to. Boy, was it loud!

I learned how to turn around a barrel, go between poles, keep a good line, and maintain a distance from the target to allow for the gun powder to bust the balloons. The goal was to be smooth and steady, not choppy. Curt set up each course for us to practice. I learned each course in the playbook. This training was fun, fast, and very loud!

Well, graduation day finally came. Curt told me that my formal training or school was over. Now he said, we will focus on competing. He told me that learning is a lifelong task because nobody knows everything. With the skills I currently had, I would keep building on them to improve. He said that daily life gives us wonderful lessons if we choose to learn from them.

Love Lesson:

The lessons displayed in this chapter represent playful love. Respect and love are demonstrated through play.

3

The Snake River Incident

It was now getting warmer outside. In fact, it was hot!

I heard Curt say that we needed to head north where it was not so hot.

Well, just a few days later, that is what we did. He loaded me in the trailer, and off we went on another adventure. This time, we were headed to some place called "Wyoming." I got a lot of practice getting in and out of that trailer on this adventure! It took us two days of driving just to get there.

Boy, was I glad when we got there! I was stiff and sore from staying in the trailer, not being able to walk around. Curt led me to a pasture with lots of nice, green grass. It was so soft, I laid down and rolled in the grass.

Awe, that felt so good.

Now, this ranch was different from where I came from. It had lots of cows and a few horses. I was used to lots of horses and no cows. I would have to learn about these ranch cows.

My cowboy, Curt, said, "I guess we will see what kind of cow sense you have while we are here". What is cow sense? I have heard of common sense but never "cow sense." Well, I would soon find out that cows are not as smart as horses! They constantly get lost, get out of the pastures, get tangled in brush, lose their mommas, and many other things. It was up to us (cowboys and horses) to get them back, get them out of the brush, and return them to their momma!

Developing cow sense was going to take some studying. I really studied these cows so I could learn as much as possible. I watched them to see who was in charge, who was always getting into things, and who I could trust. I learned how to follow their scent. Cows make lots of gas, you know! I would keep my head low so I could smell them on the grass.

My cowboy, Curt, said I had good instincts. He would get excited when I would find the cows. It seemed I was able to track them better than the other horses. He was always telling me "good job!" Huh, I did not realize this was a job, but I guess it is.

Well, one day, it rained overnight, and one of the fences fell over. About 20 cows got out of the pasture and were gone. It was our job to find them. The other cowboys' job was to fix the fence. I could smell their scent. They headed toward the river.

This was the Snake River. I had heard the other cowboys talking about this river. It was big, fast-moving, and if the cows got across it, we would probably never get them back. So, off we went at a gallop. We galloped until we got close to the river, then we slowed down.

The land was still wet from the rain, and we could see the cows' tracks. We were walking along the bank of the Snake River when suddenly, we started sinking in the soil. Boy, I have never been stuck in a sink hole before! I felt my cowboy tense up! I don't think he had ever been in a sink hole before either.

We struggled for a few minutes, trying to keep walking, but that was not working, we just kept sinking!

So, Curt said, "whoa, calm down, Easter!" He said, "I am giving you the reins, it's up to you to get us out of here!" Wow! This was the greatest and scariest challenge I had ever faced! It was up to me to get us out and save our lives.

First, I said a little prayer. I was going to need our Creator's help to get us out of this mess. Next, I took a big breath of air and jumped as high as I could. While in the air, I turned as much as I could. When we landed, I took another breath of air, jumped, and turned. Then another. I did this four times until I had us turned around and out of the quicksand!

Once we were out, I was exhausted! Curt jumped off my back and immediately began checking me out to make sure I was not hurt. He told me what an amazing thing I had just done. I felt so proud! I had never felt this pride before.

I was willing to do whatever I could to save my cowboy Curt.

Well, I know you are wondering if we found the cows, and the answer is yes. They were just over the next hill. We found them and led them back to the ranch. The other cowboys met us at the gate.

They were hooting and hollering. What an adventure!

Not only had I saved our lives but, I helped rescue 20 cows as well. I guess I do have some cow sense after all.

Love Lesson:

This adventure demonstrates unselfish love, the willingness to save the life of someone or something else.

4

Trail Ride in Southern Arizona

It was early spring, I think around April, when Curt asked if I wanted to go on a trail ride.

He was taking several other horses and riders but knew that I was up for another adventure. He had not taken me riding in the Catalina Mountains before. I was looking forward to this new adventure. So, he loaded me in the trailer, and off we went.

It was a clear day, and the sun was shining. We

started out early, so we would have plenty of day-light for the ride. There was still snow on the top of the mountain, which was such a pretty site. I looked around to see landmarks before we started just in case. I like to have a plan and know how to get back.

This was one of the lessons Curt had taught me about preparation before adventures. Always know where you are!

We first started on the trails at the bottom of the mountain. Then someone asked, "Can we go up to the snow line?"

Reluctantly Curt said, "Sure, let's go."

So, up we went. The ground was cool from all the fallen snow, and our footing was loose. I had to be very careful where I stepped. We were walking slow, but it was still challenging.

We made it to the snow line after a couple hours. There was a clearing up ahead, so we stopped for a little break. All the riders got off their horses so we could rest as well. After about 30 minutes, we started back down the mountain. The view was just as beautiful coming down the mountain as it was going up. You could see for miles and miles.

This adventure was going well until the dirt on the trail gave way. Curt and I slid about four feet down the mountain off the trail. I came to a stop. I could not move. Something was caught on my hoof!

Curt said, "Come on Easter, back up, let's go." But I did not move.

"What's wrong?" he asked, looking down at my legs. I still did not move.

Curt got off to inspect the situation. I had slid into a barbed wire fence that had fallen over from all the rain and snow. The barbed wire would cut my leg if I attempted to move it. I stayed calm, like Curt had taught me. Luckily, Curt always comes prepared. He had some wire snips in his saddle bag. He was able to cut the wire and free my leg. I was then able to back up and get back to the trail.

Our adventure was not over yet.

After we got back on the trail, the weather changed. It started snowing! At first, it was light, but then it started really coming down. The visibility was getting bad. The other riders were getting scared.

Curt reassured the others by telling them, "Easter can get us back. He has good instincts." Good thing I paid attention on the way up! Curt then let go of the reins, allowing me to get my nose to the ground. He trusted me to keep us on the trail and get us off the mountain. I walked slowly, watching every step. I had to make sure the ground did not give way like before.

Well, I led everyone safely off the mountain. It was a little dangerous at times when the trail narrowed, but everyone followed my lead. Once we made it to the bottom, Curt told me he was never happier to be at the foot of a mountain, and I agreed!

That was quite an adventure.

Love Lesson:

The love demonstrated here was trust, care, and compassion. Curt showed care and concern for Easter trapped by the wire. Easter showed care, compassion, and a willingness to save others by getting everyone off the mountain.

5

Matters of the Heart

That day started out like many other days in the Arizona dessert. There was a beautiful sunrise filled with vivid colors of yellow and red, and I thought, wow, what could be prettier than that! Little did I know that in just two hours, I would meet the prettiest horse these eyes have ever seen!

There I was, just minding my own business, when Curt pulled up with the horse trailer. You know, the one we take for our adventures. He opened the gate, and out came this gorgeous sorrel mare. She looked right at me! Her coat shined like the sunrise I had just witnessed a few hours before.

He called her 'Rojo.' I was going to call her mine!

I had never been in love before! Was this love at first sight? I thought it must be! I felt butterflies in my stomach. Now, I think that Curt had it all planned. He knew that I would fall for her. In fact, he kept walking her right by me, and he put her in a stall close to me. I was just waiting for the introduction.

Finally, after he gave her a drink of water, he walked her over to meet me. She put her head over the rail, making eye contact. She said hi. I was speechless! I could not find the words to say anything!

Curt said, "Rojo, this is Easter." He then walked her back to her stall. Our meeting was not long enough! It was short, but I felt a strong attraction already. I was looking forward to getting to know this beautiful mare.

When morning time came, Curt took Rojo out of her stall and started training her. I saw him teach her some of the same games he played with me. I was not jealous at all. She was spending time with Curt, but I did not mind. Where were these feelings coming from? She was smart and beautiful! She learned fast. Curt was very pleased with how quick she learned and how fast she ran.

Curt yelled, "Easter, she is almost as smooth as you are!" For the first time, I could see what he meant. Curt never left the saddle. She was beauty in motion.

Curt finished his training for the day and put Rojo back in her stall. He came over to me, rubbed my head, and told me that she would be going on our adventures with us. That made me happy. I was going to get to spend more time with her, you know, to work on this new relationship.

Love Lesson:

The love that Easter experienced in this chapter is called romantic love. He desired her affection and attention. He was proud of her abilities and was not jealous that she was spending time with Curt.

6

The Exhibition at the Olympics

It was time for the winter Olympics of 2002. These Olympics were going to be held in Salt Lake City, Utah. At every Olympics, they exhibit sports or events that are not part of the current Olympics. Well, this year the committee choose to exhibit Cowboy Mounted Shooting since it was an up-and-coming sport that combined equestrian events with marksmen events! The exhibition would be held about 35 miles southwest in a town named Tooele. They would also have a wild west type show during the shoot. The committee thought the fans would enjoy watching since it was so exciting, and it brought back a glimpse of the Wild Wild West. So, Curt decided to enter us.

"It was time," he said, "for another adventure."

Once again, I loaded in the horse trailer. We started the drive to Utah from Tucson, Arizona. It was snowing hard when we got to Utah, so we had to slow down. I looked out the trailer window and saw a frozen waterfall! There was also ice on the roads. The drive took longer than expected, but we finally made it.

When I got out of the trailer, everywhere I looked was a blanket of white! The mountains were all covered with snow, the buildings were all covered with snow, and I fit right in! I was white as snow! In fact, without my halter on, it was hard to see me out in the snow.

Curt had started teaching me about this new sport over the last two years, a little at a time. He also taught me about team roping, calf roping, trail riding, team penning, cutting, and reining! I have been in school since he got me!!

"Now," he said, "let's see what you have learned!"

This event was going to be six different courses, over two days. There were 100 riders all competing for the gold buckle.

I heard the announcer say, "In mounted shooting, the horse is the cowboy's most important asset. He must run smooth, not jerk. Keep a good line on the targets, not too close. Make a tight barrel turn but not knock it over."

Man, I have a hard job! Curt had prepared me for each of these tasks, now I needed to show it to the world watching.

We were in the warm-up arena getting ready for our turn on the first course. There were probably fifty other horses and riders warming up. You could feel the tension in the air. Some of the cowboys were wearing spurs to get their horse to go faster. Some were whipping their horses with the reins.

My cowboy was calm. He never raised his voice, never rode with spurs, never hit me with anything especially the reins! He simply squeezed his legs gently and touched my neck with the reins indicating which way to go.

Throughout our training, we had developed a very close connection. I was so glad that he was my cowboy! The way he treated me both there and at home was always the same. This made me want to do my very best for him. I had never realized before how important our connection was. That was a valuable lesson I learned.

It is amazing what you can learn from just watching with your eyes.

We did our very best over the next two days and the six courses. I ran my fastest, and Curt shot all the targets! We won the gold buckle! The buckle had the Olympic rings represented by horseshoes. I also won a warm horse blanket with the Olympic rings, and Curt won a leather Jacket.

However, the most important gift we won at the Olympics was honor and respect. Other horses, riders, and spectators all got to see firsthand how trust, commitment, love, and respect combine to create a wonderful outcome.

Love Lesson:

The lesson demonstrated here is trust, dedication, and commitment. Easter was able to see through the actions of others just how much he is loved, trusted, and respected. He also demonstrated self-love, a pride felt through this accomplishment.

7

A New Partnership

It was a cold winter day when Curt brought this new lady out to meet me. She was so nice, and she had such a gentle touch like Curt. She had come to see about riding me for an entire year to help her participate in the new sport of Cowboy Mounted Shooting. She needed a horse that she could shoot a gun from, and since I had years of experience with this, she wanted me.

Remember, I did win the Gold Buckle in the 2002

Olympic Exhibition shoot.

Curt explained to her that I could slow down my loping speed, which would allow her more time to cock the gun and shoot the target. He told her my lope was so smooth that her riding me would not affect her shooting; in fact, it should help her. Now, she already knew how to ride a horse, she just needed a horse not scared of the gun fire. Well, Curt agreed to let her ride me at all the major events for the 2006 season of Cowboy Mounted Shooting.

So, I went to stay in her barn.

Now, this was quite different than what I was used to. She rode me different, she talked to me different, she even fed me different! She gave me treats! She made sure that I got a bath every week. She combed my mane and tail every day and brushed my coat. She would tell me that she may not win every event, but I was going to look like a winner regardless.

Now, my coat, mane and tail are white and really hard to keep white. But working hard did not bother her! She made me shine! She showed me so much attention and affection just in the way she cared for me. I never thought I would like baths!!

So, after a couple months of practicing together and getting used to each other, we started competing in local matches. Boy, for these matches, she really dressed me up! Everything had to match! My halter, my lead rope, my saddle blanket, and my leg wraps all coordinated with her outfit! Most of the time, she wore a beautiful skirt that covered my rump. Everyone that saw us made comments on how we looked, how white and beautiful I was. Hearing those words brought on feelings of pride. I stood taller. I walked with my head up, and really felt pretty good about myself. I guess those baths were worth it.

Looking good does make you feel good, but that does not win the match.

While she was responsible for making us look good physically, I would have to help us look good technically since I was the one with experience. I made the decision to protect her while riding and to ride as fast as she could shoot. I have ridden each course before, so I knew which direction to go, and which balloons to shot first.

What, you don't think I remember each course? I do!

In fact, did you know that horses have a better memory than elephants? It's true! I remember each course because my cowboy Curt thought me them during our training days.

Now, she was an experienced rider, but she was having to learn how to shoot a single action 45 caliber gun while riding as fast as she could without missing the target! Since we were a team now, I needed to slow my gallop down to allow her enough time to shoot, especially when she made her gun change.

Wondering what a gun change is?

There are ten targets or balloons to bust, but each gun only holds enough ammo for six shots. That's why she had to change guns. They load five bullets in each gun, leaving one blank for safety. So, if I ran too fast, she might miss the target, or the gun change, and we would not win. Every miss is given five seconds in penalty points.

So, you see how important it was to shoot all the targets. This is called a clean course. Since the event was a timed event, not getting penalties was very important. Our speed would improve over time, as well as her accuracy.

Another horse fact: Did you know that horses can run up to 25 miles an hour? It is true.

Well, I am proud to report that our speed did improve over time, and she started winning buckles at the shoots. In fact, she accomplished her goal! In 2006, she won the Senior Ladies 1 World Championship title riding me! We made a really great team.

Love Lesson:

In Chapter 7, the affectionate type of love is displayed. It is love that is without romance or attraction and occurs between friends or family members. It is often referred to as "brotherly love" or mutual love, respect, and trust. What started out as a partnership to reach a goal became a great lesson of love and trust.

8

The Family Business

It's February, and time to start going to shoots!

We have spent the last three months training my daughter, Shooting Star. Curt is teaching her to be his main horse for the pistol courses and is using me for the rifle and shotgun competitions. He has to let go of the reins and shoot the lever action rifle or double barrel shotgun while still riding the course. He has taught me how to ride without a bridle and continue to run as fast as possible. Not using the reins is a piece of cake.

I love shooting in these events! In fact, Curt, and I as a team have won the World Championship in the Rifle at the 2004 and 2005 World Championships of Cowboy Mounted Shooting.

In addition to competing, I was now getting to watch and cheer for my daughter, Shooting Star. She was rapidly becoming a strong contender in the pistol competitions. I wanted her to excel more than I wanted to do it all. I was glad that Curt had another horse to ride and not always have to rely on me since I was slowing down. As a family we were getting to travel together, create memories, and develop strong bonds. I had not ever felt this type of emotional connection before. I also felt a sense of protection for my daughter. I would position myself between her and other horses. No one would bother her while I was near.

Curt was pleased with her progress. He said, "Easter, I can tell she is your daughter! She is learning very quickly, just like you did!"

Now, that made me so proud. I knew how smart

she was, but for him to notice made it that much better. I also heard him talking to another trainer who was asking him how he was able to get Shooting Star trained so quickly. Curt explained to him that it must be in the bloodline.

He said, "Easter's babies have great instincts and learn incredibly fast. They possess a higher ability to learn than some other bloodlines, and I have trained other bloodlines." He never bragged about his training techniques; in fact, he was very humble. He always credited my bloodline for the intelligence, but I know that it takes both, the willingness to learn and the abilities of a good trainer.

Curt was an amazing trainer!

Love Lesson:

The love demonstrated in this chapter is familial love. Non-romantic, deep emotional love with strong bonds and a sincere feeling of pride, the love of family.

9

I've Been Everywhere

Not many horses can say that they have been as many places and seen as much as I have. I have been on adventures that have taken me to places you cannot see by car!

I have swam in the Pacific Ocean at Pismo beach! Can you say that?

I have camped on the grounds of the Grand Canyon. Can you say that?

I have seen the lights of Vegas and the Northern Lights.

I have been to the top of mountains and walked through streams and rivers. I have felt the hot desert sand and the cold snow on my hooves. I have laid down in the softest, greenest grass you have ever seen.

How many states have you visited? I have been to Arizona, California, Nevada, Utah, Idaho, Montana, Wyoming, Colorado, New Mexico, Texas, Oklahoma, Kansas, South Dakota, Michigan, Missouri, Arkansas, Louisiana, Alabama, Mississippi, Georgia, and Tennessee. I think that is 21 states. I have also been in two other countries, Canada and Mexico!

When I was in Canada, I traveled on the Niagara Escarpment. The escarpment is most famous as the cliff over which the Niagara River plunges at Niagara Falls. This crest of rocks runs from the east to the west, from New York to Ontario. This adventure was kind of scary but very beautiful! The noise that the river makes was so loud you could not hear what anyone was saying.

Have you heard of National Parks? The National Park System encompasses 423 national park sites in the United States. They span across more than 84 million acres, with parks in each state.

My cowboy, Curt, has taken me to many of these parks. I have been to Yellowstone in Wyoming, and the Grand Teton Park in Wyoming as well. I have visited Hot Springs National Park in Arkansas. I have traveled many miles at the Saguaro National Park in Tucson, Arizona. We visited this park a lot because it was close to home. I have been to Estes Park, Colorado, which is at the base of the Rocky Mountains in Colorado.

Out of all the parks I have visited, I think I liked the Painted Desert in Arizona the best. The colors of the rocks form a rainbow that ranges from yellow to blue to red to grey. The colors are spectacular! I hope you get to visit some parks on your adventures.

In addition to scenery on my adventures, I have also met other animals! I met 16 big horn sheep in the Silver Bell Mountains at Ironwood Forest National Monument. I met elk and black bear in Wyoming. I have seen mule deer, white tail deer, and antelope in multiple states. I even chased a javelina (wild hog)!

But the strangest creature I have ever met is a Gila monster! It is a big lizard of sorts but very colorful.

Oh yeah, I can't forget my encounter with the rattlesnake. He bit me! On my leg! And I lived to talk about it!

Some of my favorite memories are from walking in parades. I have been part of the Tucson Professional Rodeo Parade called La Fiesta De Los Vaqueros. It is the largest parade where everything in it is horse drawn. There are no floats with motors. I have also walked in the Tombstone Arizona parade called Helldorado Days. This is a festival that started in 1929 and is also horse drawn. It is fun to see how life was before the invention of motors or cars. Transportation was much different back then and took a lot longer to get places.

My adventures have covered many miles and many years. I have fallen in love and have been able to experience being a daddy. I have seen my name in the record books for being the best in my sport. I have accomplished personal and professional goals beyond belief! I have made lifelong friends, both animal and human. I have seen firsthand the beauty of our country.

You think I hit the lottery? Well, I do!

Just think, if Curt had not come and rescued me from the 2T Ranch when I was a young colt, I would have been put down (killed) because of my injury. His unselfish, unconditional love allowed me to have a wonderful life full of memories and many adventures!

Love Lesson:

This chapter highlights Easter's love of adventure, and his love and pride in his Country.

10

Retirement at last

Summer had just come to an end, but the days were still hot. I was now 24 years old and not competing much at all. I wasn't as fast as I used to be, but I could still be ridden. Curt came to see me in my stall and asked if I was ready for another adventure. My ears perked up; I stood a little taller.

What adventure did he have in mind?

He said, "My sister has been wanting you to come stay on her place, Green Acres, so the grandkids can ride you. You will have the front pasture all to yourself. You won't have to stay in a stall, you can lay in the sun, be free to roam around and do whatever you want to. And she needs you to teach her husband about horses. You see, he was not raised around horses, and has a little fear. You can teach him to trust you and show him that you will not hurt him or anyone else."

What? I get to be the teacher now instead of the student? I think I am up for this adventure!

So, you guessed it. He loaded me up in the horse trailer, and off we went.

We drove for about 45 minutes, and then stopped.

"We are here!" Curt said.

Wow, that was quick. I got out of the trailer and was led to my new pasture with lots of green grass, cedar and mesquite trees, and some prickly pear cactus. Curt was right, I could go anywhere I wanted to. It was sure nice not to be confined to a stall.

Later that same day, I got to meet Marshall. I had seen him before but never really got close to him until today. He was afraid to be in the pasture with me. He did not know how to halter me or lead me.

Boy, I had my work cut out for me.

I started out slow by coming up to him at the fence during feeding time. I would put my head over the rail and make him touch me. He would pet me some but still would not get in the pasture with me.

So, one day, I moved my feed bucket away from the fence. When he came to feed me, he could not reach the bucket. The only way to feed me was to come in the pasture and get the bucket. When he was in the pasture, I came between him and the fence. I made him stop, pet me, and see that it was a safe place. Each day after that, I could sense he was feeling more comfortable being in the pasture and around me.

About a month later, Curt came by to check on me. He asked Marshall to get me from the pasture so he could trim my feet. This would be the first time Marshall had put a halter on me and led me out of the pasture. He was a little scared, but he was successful. I put my nose into the halter to show him which way it went. He buckled the strap and led me out. He kept looking down to make sure I did not step on his feet. He had really big feet! Curt showed him how to raise my feet just in case he ever needed to.

I don't think he will ever need to.

When Curt was finished trimming my feet, he asked Marshall to put me back in the pasture. Marshall led me to the pasture and was walking me to where the feed bucket was.

Curt asked, "Where are you taking him?"

Marshall replied, "To his feed bucket."

Curt said, "Just turn him loose and I will show you a trick."

Marshall turned me loose and shut the gate. I walked over to my feed bucket and was waiting for my dinner. Curt told me to get my feed bucket. So, I grabbed the bucket with my mouth and tossed it to the fence.

Curt then told Marshall, "See, you don't have to get his bucket he will get it for you! I taught him that when I first got him."

Marshall just laughed and said, "Well, I guess Easter was teaching me how to fetch!"

My life was really laid back on Green Acres. I did not have to go to competitions anymore or run fast unless I wanted to. I got up when I wanted, and I slept when I wanted. I had visitors every day! I really loved it when the grandchildren would come visit. These kids loved feeding me apples, carrots, and other treats. They would climb on the fence just to get close enough to touch my head and pat my neck. Kids are so sweet and very loving. They even liked riding me without a saddle! I could hardly tell they were on my back.

Now, having the kids around me brought out my protective instincts. These grandkids were little cowboys and cowgirls, not very tall at all. They were not afraid of me either. Sometimes, they would come to the fence without a big cowboy. I really had to watch them closely to make sure I stood still when they were near. I did not want to step on one! I would stand still until all the kids were out of the pasture, safe.

I see now that my job has drastically changed. I have become an entertainer, a celebrity, now that I am retired. Everyone that comes to visit keeps taking my picture and asks me to do tricks. They all like to see me throw my feed bucket, give rides without the use of a bridle, and pose for pictures with my left leg raised.

This new job was very rewarding. I received praise, treats, and lots of attention! I loved all three!

I think I will really enjoy retirement!

Love Lesson:

The love demonstrated in this chapter is unconditional love. Easter was allowed to live out his last days with dignity and respect. He had a wonderful life filled with adventures! Easter enriched the lives of everyone he met. He lived to be 28 years old and remained a stallion. He resided on Green Acres for 4 years. He died January 23, 2016, but his legacy continues.